Cath Maige Tuired

English translation by Morgan Daimler

The text in this book represents an original English language translation of manuscript material, based off of the older Irish manuscript.

Text copyright 2020 Morgan Daimler

ISBN: 9798551167181
Imprint: Independently published

Author's Note

The Cath Maige Tuired, often Anglicized as the Second Battle of Moytirra, is one of the most important tales in Irish mythology, telling the story of the battle between the Túatha Dé Danann and the Fomorians and providing a great deal of insight into who the Túatha Dé were. The story survived in a single 16th century manuscript called Harleian 5280 which has been translated into English several times over the last 130 years, but always with notable omissions. The initial translation was done in 1891 by Whitley Stokes but intentionally avoided passages the translator found to be difficult or obscene. A more thorough translation was done by Elizabeth Gray in 1983, however this one also omitted the more difficult poetic passages. As far as I am aware there are no existing translations into English that include the entire original text so I have undertaken to offer such here.

I am not a professional translator, nor did I learn the language in University; I am a self-taught amateur. However, I believe that there is value in offering this full text with an understanding of the difficulty and obscurity of the poetic passages. I based my own translation off of the original middle

1

Irish manuscript text as presented in both Stokes and Gray, as the two transcribed words differently in places and Gray included the Irish for the omitted passages which Stokes did not.

As with most of my translation efforts I have kept as close to the original text in tone and flow as possible and my translation is as literal as possible, including punctuation. This may feel stilted or odd to English speakers but I strongly believe that it is important to convey the feeling of the original language even in the translation. The poetic sections at times appear nonsensical and must be understood, I think, through the lens of poetry and metaphor not prose. It should also be kept in mind that as with any language in many cases multiple words can apply in translation; I have used footnotes to indicate where several options may have worked equally well or where the original may have been utilizing word play.

My hope is that this attempt will be useful for those who study the myths or who are interested in the Túatha Dé Danann.

- Morgan Daimler
  October 31, 2020

Battle of the Plain of Pillars

1 The Túatha Dé Danann were in the north of the world studying knowledge and sorcery and druidism and witchcraft and magical skill, until they surpassed the wisest in heathen skill.

2 In four cities they studied knowledge and wisdom and devilry, that is, Falias and Gorias, Murias and Findias

3 From Falias came the Fail's Stone[1] which was in Tara. It would roar beneath every king who would take Ireland.

4 From Gorias came the javelin[2] that Lugh had. No battle held out against it or against he with it in hand.

5 From Findias came Nuada's sword. No one escaped from it when it was brought

---

[1] Fail has several meanings including enclosure, fence, king, and abundance. It is also an old name for Ireland herself and we see 'men of Fail' as an expression for men of Ireland. I would suggest understanding it as 'Ireland's stone'

[2] sleg is usually given as spear, although it can mean javelin, spear, or lance. I am giving here as javelin to try to avoid the usual modern associations people have with heavy spears; the older Irish spear was a throwing spear that is lighter than many people imagine.

forth from its war-sheath and none hold out against it.

6 From Murias came the Dagda's cauldron. None went displeased[3] from it.

7 Four Druids were in the four cities there. Morfesae was in Falias. Esras was in Gorias. Uiscias was in Findias. Semais was in Murias. These here were the four poets who taught the Túatha Dé knowledge and wisdom.

8 Then the Túatha Dé made a compact with the Fomorians, and Balar son of Neit gave his daughter, that is Ethne, to Cian[4] son of Dían Cécht. She birthed then a pre-eminent[5] child, that is Lugh.

9 The Túatha Dé proceeded with a large fleet of great-ships to attack Ireland to take it by force from the Fir Bolg. They burned their ships immediately upon reaching the territory of Corcu Belgatan, that is Connemara today, so that they would not think of retreating, from the burning the smoke and mist that came from the boats filled the territory and the air all around

---

[3] dimdach can mean unsatisfied, displeased or ungrateful

[4] Cian – long enduring

[5] Buaid can have multiple meanings all relating to victorious, triumphant, advantageous, or excellent. Pre-eminent seems the best fit in this context.

them. For this it was thought they came in mist.

10 The battle of Maige Tuired (plain of pillars) was fought between [them] and the Fir Bolg and the Fir Bolg conceded and 100,000 of them were killed including their king Eochaid[6] son of Eirc.

11 In that battle there the arm of Nuada was hewn off, that is Sreng[7] son of Sengaid[8] cut it from him, Dían Cécht[9] the physician put on him a silver arm with the movement of any other arm and Credne the silver smith[10] aided in this.

12 However the Túatha Dé Danann moreover had many fall in that battle including Edleo son of Allai and Ernmas[11], and Fiachra, and Turill Bicreo.

13 After those among the Fir Bolg who escaped the battle fled to the Fomorians, and they settled on Arran and on Islay and on Mann, and on Rathlin.

14 There was contention over the sovereignty of the men of Ireland among the

---

[6] Eochaid - horseman

[7] Sreng – cord, bowstring

[8] Sengaid – thinning, fading

[9] Dían Cécht – swift power

[10] cerd here is usually given as brazier however the word means craftsman, silver or gold smith or artisan.

[11] Ernmas – iron-death

Túatha Dé and their wives[12], since Nuada could not be king after his arm was cut from him. They said it was proper to give kingship to Bres son of Elatha[13], to their own adopted son, and the compact with the Fomorians would be bound if the kingship was given to him, because the king of the Fomorians was his father, that is Elatha son of Delbeath.

15 Now then this is how the conception of Bres came to pass.

16 One of their women one day was looking at the sea and the land from a house of Maoth Sceni, that is Eriu daughter of Delbeath, she saw the sea in perfect calm the same as a smooth table. There afterwards she saw (something). Appearing to her was a silver boat. Its size seemed large but its form did not appear clearly to her, and the stream of waves carried it towards land. Then she saw in it was a man of excellent appearance. Gold-yellow hair he had to his shoulders. A cloak with ordered bands of gold thread in it. His shirt was embroidered with gold thread. A gold brooch on his breast with the shine of a precious gem in it. Two silver spears and two shafts of smooth-crafted bronze[14]. Five-circles of gold around his

---

[12] literally women
[13] Elatha — art, learned skill

neck. A gold hilted sword with silver in-layings and studs of gold.

17 The man said to her: "Shall I have an hour of copulation with you?"

"I have no tryst with you," said the woman.

"Come to the trysting, " he said.

18 They spread out [together] then. The woman wept afterwards when the man arose.

"Why do you weep?" he said.

"I have two reasons to lament," the woman said. "Parting with you, however we have joined. The youth of the Túatha Dé have vainly entreated me, and my jealous-love for you possessing me so quickly."

19 "Your distress will be removed about these two things," he said. He drew off a thumb ring of gold from his middle finger[15] and put it in her hand and told her not to part from it by sale or by gift but to the one whose finger it would fit on.

20 "There is another concern on me," she said, "that I don't know who has come to me."

---

[14] credumae – literally 'earth copper' can mean either bronze or brass

[15] I realize that this passage sounds a bit confusing, but ornasic means thumb ring and meor medhoin is middle finger.

21 "There will be no ignorance of that," he said. "Elatha son of Delbeath has come to you, king of the Fomorians. You will have a son from our sexual relations, and no name will be on him but Eochaid Bres, that is Eochaid the Shapely[16], because every shapely thing seen in Ireland, including plain and fort, ale and candle, woman and horse, will be measured in relation to that boy, so it will be said 'that is a bres."

22 Then the man went back homewards and the woman returned to her home and the well-known conception was given to her.

23 Afterwards the son was born and the name was given as Elatha had said, that is Eochaid Bres. Seven days into the woman's laying in [after childbed] there were two weeks growth on the boy, and he obtained this increase to the end of 7 years until he had obtained the growth of 14 years.

24 The result of this contention there among the Túatha Dé was that the sovereignty of Ireland went to the boy there,

---

[16] both the words Bres and Cruthach can mean fair-formed; bres usually reads as great or mighty and cruthach as fair, beautiful or shapely. In this sense what we have here is a play on words with the child being named Eochaid Bres then referred to as Eochiad Cruthach both of which can be translated as 'Eochaid the Shapely' but with different connotations.

and he gave seven hostages of the strong
men of Ireland that is his maternal kin, for
guarantors that he would return the
sovereignty if he behaved in an un-kingly
manner. His mother gave him land
afterwards and he had a fort built on the land
that is Dun Bres and it was the Dagda who
built that fort.

25 After Bres had taken the kingship, the
Fomorians – that is three Fomorian kings,
Indech[17] son of De Domnann and Elatha son
of Delbeath and Tethra[18] – imposed a tax on
Ireland, so that there was not smoke from a
house in Ireland that was not under their tax.
As well the warriors of Ireland were given to
serving them, that is Ogma under a bundle
of kindling and the Dagda a fort-builder, it
was he that built the ramparts of Bres's Fort.

26 The Dagda was grieved[19] at this work
and in the house used to ward off an idle
satirist, his name was Cridenbel, whose
mouth was in his chest[20]. Small was

---

[17] Indech - interweaving

[18] Tethra – hooded crow or the sea

[19] Toirsich can mean a variety of things including
grieved, sorrowful, or tired. We might equally render
this passage 'the Dagda was exhausted at this work'
but I have chosen to go with 'grieved' which I feel
holds the deeper context.

[20] Cridenbel literally means 'mouth-in-chest' so we
see here an example of the play on words so

Cridenbel's portion to him and large seemed the Dagda's. So he said, "Oh Dagda for your honour let the three best morsels of your portion be given to me!"

So the Dagda gave them to him every night. However the satirist's[21] portions were large, that is the morsels were each the size of a good pig. Further indeed the portions of the Dagda were a third of his serving. The appearance of the Dagda was worse for that.

27 One day then the Dagda went to the rampart and saw the Mac Óg[22] coming to him.

"Good then, oh Dagda!" said the Mac Óg.

"Indeed," said the Dagda.

"What causes such a bad aspect?" he said.

"I have a good cause," he said, "The satirist Cridenbel demands to himself every night the three best portions of my serving."

---

common in this material

[21] Cridenbel is referred to interchangeably as both a 'daul' satirist and 'cainte' satirist. It is likely that these terms originally had slightly nuanced meanings, however in general a satirist had the power to ruin a person's honour by composing a satirical poem about them

[22] This would be Oengus mac Óg, the Dagda's son. Mac Óg is usually given as either young son or son of youth

28 "I have counsel for you," said the Mac Óg. He put his hand in his pouch and took out three gold coins and gave them to him.

"Put" he said, "the three coins into the three morsels for Cridenbel tonight. Afterwards these will be the best portions on your dish and the gold will stick in his chest so that he dies of it and it will not be a good judgement by Bres afterwards. They will say to the king 'The Dagda killed Cridenbel with a hurtful herb that he gave him'. The king will then say for you to be killed. You will say to him, 'No prince's truth on you, oh king of the Feni[23], for he kept demanding of me since I started my work, and saying to me 'Give me, oh Dagda, the three morsels that are best on your plate: my income[24] is bad tonight.' I may have died of that were it not for the three coins I found today. I put them into my portion: I gave that then to Cridenbel, because it was the best thing before me, the gold. And so the gold is now in Cridenbel and he died of it.'"

---

[23] this is an archaic term and its meaning is uncertain. It may refer to the Goidelic peoples, as Gray suggests, or the Fianna.

[24] trebad, literally husbandry, ploughing, cultivation or residence however in this context it is the satirist's income or produce of the day that seems to be in discussion.

"It is certain," said the king. "Cut out the stomach from the satirist to see if we find it there. If it is not found you will die. If it is found however you will live."

30 Afterwards they cut out the stomach of the satirist, they found the three gold coins in his belly and the Dagda was saved.

31 The Dagda returned to his work the next morning and the Mac Óg came to him and he said: "You will soon finish your work and do not take payment until the cows of Ireland are gathered and take from them the black-maned, black, trained, high-spirited one year old heifer."

32 Then after the Dagda's work was finished and Bres said to him what compensation would he take for his labour. The Dagda answered: "Gather together the cows of Ireland" he said, "into one place."

The king did that as he had said and he took from them the one-year old heifer as the Mac Óg had said. That seemed a weakness to Bres. He had thought he would choose something greater.

33 Now Nuada was being treated and an arm of silver was put on him by Dian Cécht which had the movement of any hand in it. This was not good to his son, that is to Míach[25]. He went to the arm and he said

---

[25] Míach – a measure

"joint toward joint and fiber toward fiber" and healed it in three sets of three days[26]. The first three days he carried it in front of the side of his body and it was covered in skin. The next three days he carried it against his chest. The third three days he cast bright wisps of black reeds[27] after blackening in fire.

34 This was a bad healing to Dían Cécht. He threw a sword at the crown of his son's head so that it cut his skin to his flesh. The youth healed it through exercise of his craft[28]. He cut him once more and cut his flesh down to bone. The youth healed it as with the first exercise [of skill]. He struck him a third cut reaching to the membrane of his brain. The youth healed this as well with the same exercise of skill as the first. He struck then the fourth cut with certainty to his brain causing Míach to perish and Dían Cécht said that there was no physician who could heal that strike.

---

[26] the specific phrase here is téorai nómaide. Téorai can be read as three, while nómaide is used for a set of three consecutive days. Hence 'three sets of three days'

[27] boicsimin – can be read as either reeds or bulrushes.

[28] elada can mean skill, craft, learned art, science, workmanship – basically any applied craft

35 After that Dían Cécht buried Míach and three hundred and 65 herbs grew up through the burial place, under the full number of his joints and fibers. Afterwards Airmed[29] unfolded her mantle and separated the herbs there according to their proper order. Dían Cécht came and mixed the herbs, so that no one knows the healing properties but that the Holy Spirit taught them afterwards. And Dían Cécht said: "Míach is no longer; Airmed will remain."

36 Bres held the sovereignty that had been granted to him. There was a great complaining against him by his maternal kin the Túatha Dé, because there was no fat on their knives from him. However frequently they came their breath did not abound in ale. They did not see their poets nor their bards, not their satirists nor their harpers nor their pipers nor their trumpeters, nor their feat-performers[30] nor their fools entertained in his household. They did not go to contests of champions. They did not see their warriors proving their prowess before the king, but one warrior, that is Ogma son of Étaín.

---

[29] Airmed – a measure of grain

[30] clesamnach can mean a juggler or acrobat, from a word meaning feat-performer. Since juggling and acrobatics are very different in English I am choosing to go with the more general term here.

37 This was the duty on him, bringing firewood to the fort. He would bring bundles each day from the Islands of Mod [Clew Bay]. The ocean would take a third of the bundle because he was weak without food. He brought but a third and supplied the host from one time to another.

38 No continued service nor tribute came from the Tuath and the treasures of the Tuath were not given by the whole Tuath.

39 The poet went on a journey to seek lodging at the house of Bres, to wit Coirpre son of Étaín, poet of the Túatha Dé. He arrived at a house, small, constricted, black, dark moreover without a fire or equipment or bed there. An envoy brought three small cakes, indeed they were dry, on a small sad dish. He rose thereafter on the morrow, and he was not thankful.

He went then around the courtyard out of there saying:

"Without food quickly on dishes

without produce of cows on which calves grow up

without a man's dwelling place under abiding nightfall

without satisfying of storytelling guests, let this be Bres

There is nothing moreover thus in Bres," he said.

It came to pass truly as well. Nothing but decay was on him from that hour there. That was the first satire that came to pass in Ireland.

40 Afterwards the Túatha Dé went as one to talk with their adopted son, that is Bres son of Elatha, and request their sureties from him. He returned the sovereignty to them and he was not qualified after that. He begged to remain to the end of seven years.

"You will have it" said the assembly previously mentioned, "but the protection of every payment given to your hand is supported by sureties including household and land and gold and silver, herds and food and exempt from tax and payment until then."

"You will have it," said Bres, "as you have asked."

41 This is why he asked them for a delay, to gather the warriors of the fairy hills[31] that is the Fomorians, to seize the tribe by force, but [only if] he could gain a great advantage. He didn't want to be forced from his kingship.

---

[31] literally 'trenfiru an t-sidho' the strong men of the sidhe. Trenfiru is often given as warriors and has appeared previously in this text. Sidhe is not always translated but simply left as sidhe, however in this context I want to be clear that he is referring to the fairy hills or fairy mounds.

42 He went then to his mother and asked whence were his people.

"I am certain[32]" she said and went to the hill where she had seen the silver vessel on the sea. Then she went onto the strand and his mother gave him the thumb-ring that had been left with her and he put it around his middle finger and it fit him. To no person had she given it by sale or gift. It had fit on none until that day.

43 They went afterwards until they reached the land of the Fomorians. They arrived at a great plain with assemblies[33] on it. The assembly that was the greatest troop they went to. Inside the assembly there [they were] asked their story. They answered they were of the men of Ireland. They asked then if they had dogs, for at that time when hosts met in assembly it was the custom to challenge them to a hound-contest.

"We have dogs with us," said Bres. They engaged the dogs afterwards in a coursing-

---

[32] literally 'there is certainty on me'

[33] airecht is more accurately translated as court, as in a royal court, but can be read in a general sense as a gathering or assembly with the understanding it would include freemen and nobles. Or as the eDIL says: "*name given to the public assembly of freemen and later of the more important families in the territory whose functions included the transaction of certain important legal business*" (eDIL, 2020)

match and the dogs of the Túatha Dé were swifter than the dogs of the Fomorians. The question was put on them then if they had horses to race.

They answered. "We have." And their horses were swifter than the horses of the Fomorians.

44 They asked then if they had anyone skilled when it came to swordplay. None was found with them but Bres alone. However when he raised the hand with the sword his father saw the thumb ring on his finger and asked who that warrior was. His mother answered for him and said that he was the king's son. She told the story as it has been recounted so far.

45 There was sadness on his father for him. His father asked "What powerful force brought you out of the land you were ruling?"

Bres answered, "Nothing took me but my own unfairness and inordinate pride. I deprived them of their treasures and valuables and their own food. No tax or payment has been taken from them before."

46 "That is unfortunate[34]," said his father. "Better their prosperity than your kingship.

---

[34] dúaig has several meanings ranging from ill-fated to malevolent to unfortunate or bad.

Better their prayers than their curses. Why then came you?" asked his father

47 "I have come requesting warriors from you", he said. "I will take the land there by force."

48 "You should not take by injustice what you could not take by justice," he said.

49 "A question for you, what counsel is there for me?" said Bres.

50 Afterwards he sent him to the warrior, Balor grandson of Neit, king of the Islands[35] and to Indech son of Domnann king of the Fomorians and they gathered from Lochlann[36] westwards all the hosts to Ireland, to impose tax and kingship on them by force, making a single causeway of ships from foreign lands[37] to Ireland.

51 There never came to Ireland a host that was more loathsome or monstrous than the host of the Fomorians. There was contention between the men of the shields of

---

[35] the Islands – na Innis – is often used idiomatically to mean the Hebrides.

[36] Lochlann is a general term for any Viking territory or any area north-west, but is often also used idiomatically for supernatural realms.

[37] here literally 'Gall' which can mean everything from Scandinavian lands to the Hebrides to Gaul. The wider context is a foreign place, ie not Ireland, so that is the meaning I have gone with here.

Lochlann[38] and the foreigners of the Islands about that hosting.

52 However as to the Túatha Dé that is examined here.

53 Nuada was, after Bres, again in the kingship of the Túatha Dé. He gave a great feast for the Túatha Dé at Tara in due time. There was a certain young warrior[39] advancing towards Tara, Samildánach was his name. There were doorkeepers in Tara then, that is Gamal son of Figail and Camal son of Riagail were their names. When the

---

[38] Gray gives this as 'from Scythia of Lochlann' because the original text capitalizes Sgiathia. In older Irish Scythia would be Scithia and the adjective having shields or of the shields would be sciathag or sciathach. The text in typical CMT fashion gives us a word that is neither of those. I am choosing to interpret both sgiathia and gall (in the following sentence), despite the capitalizations as adjectives rather than use 'Scythians of Lochlann' which is somewhat nonsensical given the actual physical locations of those places.

[39] Lugh's youth is emphasized here with the phrase 'óglaech óg' which may be read as young warrior; óg means youth or young person among other things laech means warrior (among other things); óglaech is often read as youth or young person. In this case I am giving it as warrior to avoid saying 'young youth' which is awkward and because I believe the original intent is more along the lines of emphasizing his youth as a warrior.

latter was there, he saw an unknown troop approaching. A handsome, shapely young warrior with a king's garment[40] was at the front of them.

54 They asked the doorkeeper to announce their coming to Tara. The doorkeeper asked, "Who is coming there?"

55 "Lugh Lonnansclech has come here, son of Cian son of Dían Cécht and Ethne daughter of Balor, foster-son of Tailtiu daughter of Magmor[41] king of Spain and rough Eochaid son of Duach."

56 The doorkeeper inquired of the Samildánach[42]: "What skill do you have?" he said, "because no one enters Tara without a skill."

57 "Quickly ask me," he said, "I am a carpenter."

The doorkeeper answered, "We do not need you. We already have a carpenter, that is Luchta son of Luachada."

---

[40] Imscigg is a form of imscing which can mean everything from a pavilion, bed, couch to a garment or diadem. Gray gives this as diadem here, and it may well be but I am choosing to go with garment as I find it less intuitive for Lugh to be wearing a crown at this point in the story but kingly dress seems to make sense.

[41] Magmor = great plain

[42] Samildánach may best be understood as 'many-joined-skills'

58 He said, "Ask again, oh doorkeeper, I am a smith."

The doorkeeper answered him: "We already have a smith, that is Colum Cuaolleinech[43] of the three new-workings."

59 He said: "Ask again, I am a champion."

The doorkeeper answered: "We do not need you: we already have a champion, that is Ogma son of Ethlend[44]."

60 He said again: "Ask again," he said, "I am a harper."

"We do not need you: we already have a harper, that is Abchan son of Bicelmos who was chosen by the men of the three Gods in the fairy mounds."

61 He said: "Ask again, I am a warrior."

The doorkeeper answered: "We do not need you. We already have a warrior, that is Bresal Able-Handed[45] son of Echdach Reckless-Handed[46]."

62 He said then, "Ask again, oh doorkeeper, I am a poet and a storyteller."

---

[43] cuaolleinech may possible be read as stick faced, cuaoll = bundle of sticks, einech = face. Make of that what you will.

[44] Almost certainly the same as Ogma son of Étaín mentioned earlier

[45] Echerlam

[46] Báethláim

"We do not need you: we have a poet and historian already, that is En[47] son of Ethomain."

63 He said, "Ask again," he said, "I am a sorcerer[48]."

"We do not need you: We have sorcerers already: numerous are our druids and people of power."

64 He said, "Ask again, I am a physician."

"We do not need you: we have Dían Cécht as our physician."

65 "Ask again," he said, "I am a cupbearer."

"We do not need you: we have cupbearers already that is Delt and Drucht and Daithe, Taei and Talom and Trog, Glei and Glan and Glesi[49]."

---

[47] En - water

[48] Corrguinech, a specific type of practice. The term breaks down to corr – crane and guinech – wounding, ie crane-wounding and is usually said to be done on one foot, with one hand behind the back and one eye closed. We will see Lugh's skill in this form of magic showing up later in the story

[49] Delt – name of a river

Drucht - dew

Daithe – light, or swiftness

Taei - birth

Talom = earth

Trog – birth or offspring, related to trogain

23

66 He said, "Ask again: I am a good artificer."

"We do not need you: we already have an artificer, that is artificer Credne."

67 He said to him again: "Ask the king," he said, "whether he has one man who possesses all these skills and if he has I will not enter Tara."

68 Then the doorkeeper went to the king's house and told the king all of this. "A young warrior has come before us for hospitality," he said, "Samildánach and all the skills which serve your people he has all of them in one, so that he is the man of every whole skill."

69 He said then that they should bring the fidchell[50] boards of Tara to him there, and he won the stakes, until he made the enclosure of Lugh. But if it was in the time of the battles of Troy that fidchell was created it had not arrived in Ireland then. The same time was on the battle of Maige Tuired and Troy's destruction[51].

Glei – clear, bright

Glan - pure

Glesi - brightness

[50] Fidchell a game similar to chess

[51] Or put another way the events occurred at the same time. This explicit correlation between Irish mythological events and those in classical (or Biblical) literature is a typical device to tie the story

70 This was then told to Nuada there. "Let him come in the courtyard," Nuada said, "Because no man has come before like that to this fort."

71 Afterwards the doorkeeper let him pass and he went into the fort, and he sat in the scholar's seat, because he was a master of all skills[52].

72 Afterwards Ogma threw the great flagstone, which needed the effort of four twice-twenty[53] yokes [of oxen], through the hall so that it was against Tara outside: this was a challenge to Lugh. Lugh threw it back to the centre of the king's house, and he threw the fragment [of the wall] in a feat back outwards in the king's house so that it was whole.

73 "Let a harp be played for us," said the assembly. Afterwards the young warrior played sleep-music for the assembly and the king the first night. They fell asleep from that time until the same time the next day. He played sorrowful-music so they were

---

to human history and to a well known foreign story.
[52] sui can be read as 'master, scholar, sage, or expert'. I am choosing to give it first as scholar and then as master but it should be understood that these are the same words in Irish and convey the wider meaning of all the listed terms.
[53] the text reads cetri XX which Gray gives as fourscore or eighty.

lamenting and mournful. He played laughing-music so that they were happy and rejoicing.

74 Afterwards Nuada considered, seeing the many powers of the youth, whether he could remove from them from the oppression they suffered with the Fomorians. So they held a council about the young warrior. The decision to which Nuada arrived, a friendly exchange of seats with the young warrior. Samildánach went to the king's seat and the king rose before him until the end of 13 days[54].

75 Then he conversed with two brothers, that is the Dagda and Ogma, at Grellach Dollaid the next day. He summoned to them his two kinsmen[55], that is Goibhniu and Dían Cécht.

76 A full year was spent by them in secret conference there, so that Grellach Dollaid was known as Amrun of the men of the Gods[56].

---

[54] the thirteen days does not seem to be literal but rather may represent a ritual period of some sort.
[55] the same word 'brathair' is used in both sentences. It can mean brother, cousin, or kinsmen. In this case it is clear from the stories that the Dagda and Ogma are brothers, and since Dían Cécht is Lugh's grandfather 'kinsmen' seems more appropriate there. However the 'he' in the text is somewhat ambiguous.

77 Then they summoned to them the druids of Ireland and the physicians and charioteers and smiths and hospitallers, and judges. They conversed together secretly.

78 Afterwards he inquired of the sorcerer[57] that is Mathgen[58] was his name, what power he would wield. He said he would shake the mountains of Ireland under the Fomorians, so that the tops would go to the ground. And it would appear to them the principle mountains of the lands of Ireland were on the side of the warriors of the Túatha Dé Danann, that is Sliab Liag and Denda Ulad and Bennai Boirche [the Mourne Mountains] and Bri Ruri and Sliab Baldmai and Sliab Snechtae, Sliab Mis and Blai-slaib and Nemthenn [Nephin Mountains] and Sliab Maccu Belgodon and

---

[56] Grellach Dollaid – grellach means swamp or bog. Dollaid possibly from dolaid, distress, ergo swamp of distress
Dea may be read as either goddess or gods. Amrun is an uncertain word, but may incorporate the word rún 'secret'.
[57] sorcerer is the usual translation here which I am also using however it should be noted that the original term is corrguinecht, literally 'crane wounding one', a term which has specific connotations of cursing magic or battle magic
[58] Mathgen – good birth

Segois [Curlieu Hills] and Cruachan Aigle [Croagh Patrick].

79 He asked the cupbearer, what power he would wield? He said he would bring the twelve principle lakes of Ireland into their presence and they would find no water no matter how thirsty they were. These are the lakes: Derc-loch, Loch Luimnigh, Loch n-Orbsen, Loch Ri, Loch Mescdhae, Loch Cuan, Loch Laeig, Loch n-Echach, Loch Febail, Loch Dechet, Loch Rioach, Marloch. They would go to the twelve primary rivers of Ireland that is Buas, Boann [Boyne], Banna, Nem, Lai, Sinann [Shannon], Muaid, Sligech [Sligo], Samair, Fionn, Ruirtech, Siuir, and they would be hidden from the all the Fomorians so they would not find a drop in them. Drink would be provided for the men of Ireland however even if the battle went seven years.

80 The druid Firgol mac Mamois said: "Three showers of fire will be poured down upon the faces of the Fomorian host and I will take two third-parts of their valour and skill at arms and power from them and I will bind their urine in their bodies and the bodies of their horses. Each breath exhaled from the men of Ireland shall increase their strength and skill at arms and power. Even if the battle lasts to the end of seven years they will be without weariness at all."

81 The Dagda said: *"The power that you boast I shall do all myself."*

"You are the Good God[59]!" they all said, 'Dagda' was on him from that time on.

82 They disbanded then the council there to meet the same day in three years.

83 Afterwards when the preparations for the battle had been made there, Lugh and Dagda and Ogma went to the three Gods of Danann and they gave Lugh weapons for the battle and they had been preparing for seven years and creating weapons.

"Undertake a battle of overthrowing," so sang the goddess Morrigan turning to Lugh, "Awake,[60] make a hard slaughter, smiting bodies, attacks boiling, greatly burning, devastating, the people to a man crying out,. Awake."

Firgol mac Mámais the young druid was there prophesying the battle and strengthening the Túatha Dé, so that there he said: "Battle will be realized, the fire wave

---

[59] Dagda literally means 'good god' but not good in any moral sense but rather good as in excellent. The word dag means good but is also used as an intensifier like 'very', and is used in word compounds without any moral implications.

[60] this passage, specifically the Morrigan's incitement of Lugh is not usually translated. Gray gives only up to 'Awake' then stops. Stokes omits the entire passage.

of battle, the sea ebbs green-waved not to be revived a great amount guarding a dense forest Lug Lamfhadae will avenge. The great hero Ogma is eager to break the phantom sea to him after a living king. Engaged in exacting tribute, celebrating lives, coming an enclosure is obtained, a plain of forts, a milk territory. Freemen with territory each in sovereignty a plain. Long lasting offering they are gathering territory, freemen with territory each without anyone being a serf; from Nuada fierce-eyed surpassing the point of battle, and battle will be realized."[61]

84 The Dagda had a house at Glenn Etin in the north. The Dagda was to meet a woman on a day, yearly, about Samhain of the battle at Glen Etin.

The Unish of Connacht calls by the south. The woman was at the Unshin of Corand washing her genitals, one of her two feet by Allod Echae, that is Echuinech, by water at the south, her other by Loscondoib, by water at the north. Nine plaits of hair undone upon her head.

---

[61] this passage in its entirety is usually not translated. Gray stops after 'Battle will be waged…"; Stokes omits this entire section, skipping from the Lugh, the Dagda, and Ogma going to the three gods of skill to the Dagda going to Glen Etin.

The Dagda spoke to her and they made a union. Lying Down of the Married Couple[62] was the name of that place from then. She is the Morrigan, the woman mentioned particularly here.

85 Afterwards she commanded[63] the Dagda to strip his land, that is Mag Scetne, against the Fomorians, and told the Dagda to call together the aes dana of Ireland to meet at the Ford of Unshen and she would go to Scetne and injure with magic the king of the Fomorians, that is Indech mac De Domnann is his name, and she would take the blood of his heart and kidneys of his battle-ardor from him. Because of that she would give to the gathered hosts the blood in her two palms, striking, groaning, warlike by the Ford of Unshen. Ford of Utter Destruction was its name afterwards because of the magical injury done to the king

86 Afterwards the aes dana did that and they recited incantations against the host of the Fomorians.

---

[62] Lige ina Lánamhnou = lige – verbal noun of laigid; meaning lying down; ina of the; lánamhnou form of lanamain, married couple

[63] Itbert can mean a variety of things including said or told but it also has connotations of commanding which is how I am choosing to interpret it here. I feel this best fits the context of the passage.

87 This was a week[64] before Samhain and they all scattered until all the men of Ireland came together the day before Samhain. Six times thirty hundred were their number that is twice thirty hundred in every third.

88 Then Lugh sent the Dagda to spy[65] against the Fomorians and delay them until the arrival of the men of Ireland to the battle.

89 The Dagda went afterwards to the encampment of the Fomorians and asked for a delay of battle from them. This was given as he'd asked. The Fomorians made porridge for him and this to make a fool of him, because there was a great love of porridge on him. They filled the five-fists-deep cauldron of the king for him, they mixed in four-twenty measures of new-milk and equal measures of flour and fat. They put goats, and sheep, and pigs into it and boiled them all together. They poured it into a hole in the earth and Indech said to him that death would be inflicted on him unless he ate all of it, so that he wouldn't give slander to the Fomorians with use of his unfair advantage[66].

---

[64] sechtmad, literally a period of seven days

[65] tascélad can mean spy, scout, or observe. All of these may apply here.

[66] the implication here seems to be that the

90 He took then his ladle and it was suitable in size for a couple to lay in the middle of the ladle. These were the bits in it, a half of slated pig and quarter of fat.

91 Then the Dagda said: "This is good food if the broth doesn't spoil the taste." Then he put the full ladle in his mouth, he said: "It's not spoiled by its inferior portions, says the elder."

92 He took his bent finger over the bottom of the hole in the residue between clay and sand. He fell asleep afterwards when he'd eaten his porridge. As big as a house cauldron was his belly, and the Fomorians laughed at their success.

93 He went from them then to Tracht Eba. Not easy going for the warrior because of the great size of his belly. His appearance was ugly. He had a cowl to the bend of his two elbows. A grey-ish tunic to the middle of the curve of his arse. A pronged pole on wheels was the effort of eight [men] to bring, and sufficient was its track for the boundary ditch between provinces. It is called 'Staff Track of the Dagda'[67].

Fomorians were mocking the Dagda for his appetite and implied he might accuse them of lack of hospitality if they didn't give him an immense meal.
[67] this can equally be read as 'penis track of the Dagda' as lorg means both staff/club/wand and penis. It is highly likely this was meant as a double

Uncovered was his long penis. Two shoes of horse skin on him with the hair outside.

He journeyed on and saw a maiden in front of him, the girl had a distinguished figure on her. Her hair was beautiful. The Dagda desired her, but for the blemish that was the size of his belly. The girl took to screaming at him then the girl wrestled with him. She threw him so that he fell to the curve of his arse in the earth. He looked fiercely at her and said, "What reason is on you," he said, "to throw me from my rightful path?"

"This reason was on me: to get you to carry me on your back to the house of my father."

"Who is your father?" he said.

"I am the daughter," she said, "of Indech mac De Domnann."

She leapt on him again and struck him forcefully, so that the furrow filled around him with the excrement from his belly; and she satirized him so he would carry her on his back, three times. He said he had a prohibition[68] to carry anyone who didn't call him by his name.

---

entendre.

[68] literally a geis, a kind of kind of prohibition relating to a thing that either must be done or must not be done to avoid Otherworldly retribution.

"What name is on you?" she said.

"Fer Benn[69]," he said.

"Excessive is the name!" she said. "Arise, carry me on your back, oh Fer Benn."

"That is not my name, truly," he said.

"What is?" she said.

"Fer Benn Bruach," he said.

"Arise, carry me on your back, oh Fer Benn Bruach," she said.

"That is not my name, truly," he said.

"What is?" she said. He told her all of it. Immediately she went and said, "Arise, carry me on your back, oh Fer Benn Bruach Brogaill Broumide Cerbad Caic Rolaig Builc Labair Cerrce Di Brig Oldathair Boith Athgen mBethai Brightere Tri Carboid Roth Rimairie Riog Scotbe Obthe Olaithbe[70].

---

[69] Horned man or man of the peaks

[70] the names of the Dagda are complex, some clearly being words and others more obscure.

Fer Benn – man of the peaks or peaked man. Benn may also be read as the horn of an animal.

Broumide is also uncertain but may be a compound of bró and mide, millstone and middle

Cerbaid is a verbal noun that means to hack or cut off.

Caic is a form of cacc, excrement.

Rolaig is a form of leach, warrior, with ro added as an intensifier.

Buile may be a form of baile, madness, or buille

Rude king, I think, contentious looking rooted-honour[71]. Arise, carry me away from this place!"

"Do not mock or strike me more, oh girl," he said.

---

stroke or chime; buile may also be a form of builce meaning stomach

Labair relates to being loud, noisy, boastful

Cerrce is uncertain but may possibly mean 'striker'

Di bríg is a phrase possibly meaning 'greatly worthy'

Oldathair a form of ollathair, great or ample father.

Boith is a form of baeth meaning both silly, foolish, reckless as well as wanton or sexual open.

Athgen mBethai may mean "regeneration of the world

Brightere may be a compound of bríg, valuable/powerful, and tír, territory or land.

Tri Carboid Roth is uncertain but may mean three chariot wheels.

Rimaire is also uncertain but could mean either 'retelling' or 'bad weather' if it is related to the word rím

Ríog is a form of the word for king.

Scotbe may relate to judgement. Isolde Carmody suggests that these three should be read together to give us 'enumerating a king's speech' or less literally enumerating judgements (Carmody, 2012).

Obthe Olaithbe could mean 'refusal of the great ebb'

[71] This sentence is not translated by either Gray or Stokes. I am offering my best suggestion on its meaning but the words are obscure and opaque making understanding difficult.

"It will be difficult, indeed," she said.

Afterwards he got up from the hole after releasing his belly. And moreover the girl had waited a long time for that. He arose then and took the girl on his back; and put three stones in his belt. And each stone fell from it in time – and it has been said that they were his genitals which fell from it. The girl lept on him and struck his arse and her pubic hair was bared. Afterwards the Dagda was able to have her as his mistress and they made love then. The site remains at Tracht Eoboile where they joined together.

The girl then said to him, "You will not go to the battle however you try to go," the woman said.

"I will go surely," said the Dagda.

"You will not go," said the woman, "I will be a stone at the mouth of each ford as you go."

"That will be true," said the Dagda, "But you will not keep me from it. I will walk powerfully on each rock, and the imprint of my heel will be on each rock forever."

"That will be true, but they will be overturned so that you cannot see them. You will not go by me until I have summoned the sons of Tethra from the fairy mounds. Because I will be a large oak in each ford and each road you shall go."

"I will go surely," said the Dagda. "And the track of my ax will be on every oak forever." (and people have talked of the track of the Dagda's ax)

Then she said, "Permit the Fomorians to land," she said, "as the men of Ireland all have gathered in one place." She said moreover that she would hinder the Fomorians, and chant against them, and practice the deadly craft of the branch[72] on them – and she would take on alone a ninth part of the host.

94 Afterwards the Fomorians went until their tenths were in Scetne. The men of Ireland were in Maige Aurforlaigh. Then were the two hosts threatening battle. "Do the men of Ireland venture to give battle to us," said Bres son of Elatha to Indech mac De Domnann.

"I will give the same," said Indech, "so small will their bones be in pieces [unless they] bestow their tax."

95 To have protection on him the men of Ireland were agreed not to let Lugh in to the battle. His nine teachers[73] had come to guard

---

[72] this word is obscure, gice, probably gicce which is usually seen with gabul in a compound meaning a forked pole. Here it appears alone, likely meaning a pole or branch. Gray suggests 'wand' but there is no precedent for that usage so I am going with the more literal.

him, that is, Tollus-dam and Ech-dam and Eru, Rechtaid, Fionn, and Fosadh and Fedlimidh, Iubot and Scibar and Minn[74]. They feared for him an early death for the young warrior because of his many skills. Because of that they did not let him go to the battle.

96 The nobles of the Túatha Dé Danann were gathered around Lugh. He asked his smith, that is Goibhniu, what power he would wield for them.

97 "Not hard," he said. "Even though the men of Ireland are in battle to the end of seven years, [any] spear that separates from its shaft there, or sword that breaks there, I will give a new weapon to replace it. No spear-point made by my hand," he said, "will miss its cast. No body chosen by it will

---

[73] Gray gives oide here as foster fathers, however the standard meaning is teacher and I have chosen to go with that instead.

[74] Tollus-dam roughly perhaps 'piercing champion'
Ech-dam horse-champion
Eru refusal
Rechtaid judge or lawgiver
Fionn white, bright, shining one
Fosadh steadfast
Fedlimidh uncertain, possibly 'sharp-whistling'
Iubor yew wood
Scibar pepper
Minn oath, halidom, badge of honour

experience life afterwards. This great deed Dolb, smith of the Fomorians, cannot do. I am concerned with preparation for the battle of Maige Tuired now."

98 "And you, oh Dían Cécht," said Lugh, "What power can you control?"

99 "Not hard," he said: "Any man who is injured there, unless his head is cut from him, or except if the membrane of his brain or his spinal cord is cut, he will be whole in the battle the following day."

100 "And you, oh Credne," said Lugh to his craftsman, "What power is yours in battle?"

101 "Not hard," said Credne. "Rivets for spears and hilts for swords and bosses for their shields and their shafts I will supply them all."

102 "And you, oh Luchta," said Lugh to his carpenter, "What power is with you in the battle?"

103 "Not hard," said Luchta, "a sufficiency of shields and spear shafts I will supply them all."

104 "And you, oh Ogma," said Lugh to his champion[75], "What power is yours in battle?"

---

[75] trenfer literally means 'strong man' and is often given as warrior or champion. It has appeared throughout this text usually translated as warrior.

105 "Not hard," he said, "Matching the king and matching three-nines (27) of his friends, and taking the battle for a third of the men of Ireland."

106 "And you, oh Morrigan," said Lugh, "What power?"

107 "Not hard," she said, "Pursue what was observed, pursue to strike down, I control bloody destruction."

108 "And you, oh sorcerers," said Lugh, "what power?"

109 "Not hard," said the sorcerers, "the white soles of their feet will be seen after they are overthrown by our craft, so that killing them will be a gift and we will take two-thirds of their strength from them, and keep back their urine in them."

110 "And you, oh cupbearers," said Lugh, "what power?"

111 "Not hard," said the cupbearers, "We will give a great thirst to them and they will not find enough to quench it."

112 "And you, oh Druids," said Lugh, "what power?"

113 "Not hard," said the druids, "we will bring showers of fire on the faces of the Fomorians so that they cannot look upwards, the rightly-piercing power of the warriors will kill them in the battle."

114 "And you, oh Coirpre son of Étaín," said Lugh to his poet, "what power can you control in battle?"

115 "Not hard," said Coirpre, "I will make a satire on them and lampoon them, and shame them, so they will offer no resistance to the warriors through the incantations of my skill."

116 "And you, oh Bé Chuille[76] and Dinand," said Lugh to his two witches[77], "What power is with you in the battle?"

117 "Not hard," they said, "We will use our sorcery on the trees and stones and *clods* of earth, so they will be a host under arms against them and they will flee in fright and terror."

118 "And you, oh Dagda," said Lugh, "what power is yours against the Fomorians in battle?"

119 "Not hard," said the Dagda, "I will fight for the men of Ireland with mutual-cutting and destruction and witchcraft. Like many fragments of hail under the feet of horses their bones will be under my club

---

[76] Bé chuille – possibly destructive woman
[77] witches here is specifically ban-tuathaig a type of witch who would have been associated with counterclockwise or northward movements and by extension possibly cursing

where the attack of the two enemies meets on the battlefield of Maige Tuired."

120 Indeed did Lugh address each in turn about their skills towards destruction, and was strengthening and addressing the host so that the spirit of a king or great chief was in every man from under their distress.

121 Then the battle was ordered every day between the people of the Fomorians and the Túatha Dé, but the enemies were not kings or kingly warriors waging it, but keen, arrogant people [were the] enemies.

122 There was a wonder then to the Fomorians, a certain thing in the battle. Blunted were their arms, that is their spears and their swords, and the dead men did not come back from being weapons-killed. That was not so with the Túatha Dé, however blunted were their weapons one day they were restored[78] the next, because Goibniu the smith was in the workshop making swords[79] and spears and lances, he would create these weapons with three blows. Then

---

[78] atgainidis is a form of adgainethar which literally means 'reborn'. I am going with restored here, as does Gray, because the idea of a weapon being reborn may sit oddly with some readers. However the text can be read this way.

[79] calc is a form of colg which is often given as sword but unlike claideb which means 'slashing style sword' colg can mean any pointed or sharp weapon

Luchta the carpenter created the shafts with three cuttings and the third cut was a smoothness and would insert them in the socket of the spear-head. Since the weapons were in the side of the workshop he would throw the socket with the spear-shaft and there was no need to set them again. Then Credne the craftsman would create the rivets with three strokes, and he would throw the sockets of the spears at them and it was not needed to spike holes for them and [they] remained thus.

123 This then is what was used to heat the wounded warriors there, so that the next day they were iron-bound[80] because of Dían Cécht and his two sons and his daughter, that is Ochtriuil and Airmed and Míach, nearby composing incantations over gushing water, that is the Sláine its name. Throwing their severely wounded in it, indeed in the great vessel. They would be alive emerging out of it. Their severely wounded would be healthy through the strength of the chanting of the four healers who were around the well.

124 Then it went against the Fomorians there, so they chose a man to inspect the

---

[80] iarnauharach is given by Gray as 'more fiery' however it seems to be a compound of iarnach [iron-made] and arach [bound or tied]

battle and the behaviour of the Túatha Dé, that is Rúadán[81] son of Bres and Brighid daughter of the Dagda. Because he was a son and a grandson of the Túatha Dé. Afterwards he told the Fomorians about the work of the smith and the carpenter and the craftsman and the four healers that were around the well. They sent him back to kill one of the people of skill, that is Goibniu. He requested a spear from him, its rivets from the craftsman, and its shaft from the carpenter. All was thus given as he had asked. Moreover there was a woman there grinding weapons that is Crón[82] mother of Fíanlug[83], and she sharpened Rúadán's spear. The spear was given to Rúadán by his maternal kin, so that 'spear of the maternal kin' is what the weaver's beam is called in Ireland.

125 Rúadán turned around after he was given the spear and wounded Goibhniu. He drew out the spear and cast it at Rúadán, it flew through him and he died of it in front of his father in the assembly of the Fomorians.

---

[81] Rúadán means both a reddish brown colour and a type of wheat

[82] Crón is a colour described as a reddish brown or yellow

[83] Fían – member of the Fianna, lug a warrior or hero, hence I might suggest fíanlug may mean 'warrior of the Fianna'

Brighid came and keened her son. She screamed loudly and finally wept. This was the first time that weeping and loud screaming were heard in Ireland. And she was thus the Brighid that had devised a whistling to signal by night.

126 Then Goibhniu went into the well and he was healed. There was a warrior among the Fomorians, that is Octriallach son of Indech son of Domnann king of the Fomorians. He said to the Fomorians that they should bring a stone, every single man, from the stones of the [river] Drobesa to throw into the well of Sláine at Achad Abla to the west of Maige Tuired, to the east of Loch Arboch. They went and each man brought a stone into the well. The Cairn of Octraillach[84] was what the cairn was [called]. Another name however for that well was Loch Luibe[85], because Dían Cécht has put in it every herb that was named in Ireland.

127 When it came therefore time to join the great battle the Fomorians arose forth from their encampment and formed strong battalions that were indestructible. There was not a chief nor valorous man among them without a breastplate against his skin,

[84] Modern day Heapstown Cairn
[85] loch luibe literally lake of herbs

without a helmet on his head, without a clamorous[86] sharp spear in his right hand,, without a keen-edged sword for his belt, without a strong shield on his back. It was 'striking a head against a cliff', it was 'a hand in a snakes' nest', it was 'a face in fire' to [try to] defeat the host of the Fomorians at that time.

128 These were the kings and chiefs who kept up strengthening the host of the Fomorians, that is Balor son of Doit son of Net, Bres son of Elatha, Tuirie Tortbuillech son of Lobois, Goll and Irgold, Loscennlom son of Lomglionigh, Indech son of Domnan king of the Fomorians, Octriallach son of Indech, Omna and Bagna, Elatha son of Delbaeth.

129 The Túatha Dé Danann arose on the other side and left Lugh with his nine companions guarding him, and went to kindle the battle. Thereafter when the battle was sought Lugh departed from those guarding him and went as a chariot-fighter, he was in front of the battalions of the Túatha Dé. Then a keen, cruel conflict was waged between the men of the Fomorians and the men of Ireland. Lugh was exhorting

---

[86] this word is usually not translated, muirnig, however it appears to be a variant of muirnech meaning tumultuous, clamorous, mettlesome

the men of Ireland; to give battle vehemently, so they wouldn't be in captivity forever. Better to find a portion of death while protecting their ancestral land than to be under captivity and under tribute like they had been. So upon his cloak Lugh sang this to intervene, on one foot and one eye[87], encompassing the men of Ireland.:

"Fight[88] a slaughterous battle! There is fierce battle, a contentious, cutting army contending before armies of phantoms, men of the land beware. Aligning to truth without choice, following furies. Bursting forth, overthrowing, dividing, black truth: little white death-ring, Hale! Hale! Woe! Woe! Sinister[89]! Fierceness! A sanctified omen after cloud-shadows our fame will be spread through armies by triple skilled Druids. I am not reduced by battles at borders: wounding, matched, slender-speared, sky ravaging, deadly brilliance, burning, greatly subduing them, greatly thundering, the sun rises.

---

[87] the portion following this is untranslated by Gray; Stokes stops after 'fight!' which he gives as arise
[88] this is almost always translated as "arise" under the assumption it's an irregular form of atraig "to arise" however I personally feel that its a variation of airgal "to fight, do battle; overcome". The third possibility is at-roí "to fail" but that is difficult to see in context
[89] also may mean left or leftwards

Asking each nine of them, in the presence of Ogma and also in the presence of sky and earth, in the presence of sun and moon. A band of warriors is my company for you. My army is a great army, ramparts here, fleet-footed, seething, strong-guarding, choosing, may we fight a slaughterous battle! Fight!"[90]

130 A great cry was given by the hosts as they went to battle, they came together then, and each began to strike their opposites.

131 A great many beautiful ones fell there in the enclosure of death. Great the slaughter and the grave-laying that was there. There was arrogance and shame-facedness side by side. There was wrath and rage. Plentiful were the streams of blood over the bright-skin of young warriors there weapon-wounded by the hands of those rushing to go through stress[91] for shame. There was a rough, tumultuous sound and a multitude slashing and the valorous warriors engaged in protecting their spears and their shields and their bodies while being struck by their opposites who were smiting with

---

[90] This chant which is made in a crane pose, on one foot, with one closed, seems to be an example of Corrguinecht which Lugh has previously said he was a master of.

[91] Gray gives this as 'danger' but alternate meanings are stress and need

their spears and their swords. Rough, as well, the noise there throughout the battlefield, that is the shouting of warriors and the din of shields, brightness and whistling[92] of the swords and the ivory blades, the clatter and rattling of the quivers, whistling and whizzing of the small spears[93] and lances, and uproarious smiting of weapons.

132 Indeed when they met their fingers and feet were mutually striking, they were falling from standing because of the slipperiness[94] of the blood under the feet of the soldiers, and having their heads hewn from them as they sat. Risen up was a gory, injurious, pointed, bloody battle and spear shafts[95] were reddened in the hands of enemies.

---

[92] fedgairi I am assuming here is fetgaithe, which means the sound a sword makes when it cuts through the air

[93] foga a small spear, distinct from other types of Irish fighting spears

[94] literally sliminess

[95] note that the word for spear shafts used here 'unnsenn' is capitalized in Stokes manuscript but not in Gray's. When capitalized we may perhaps suggest this was meant as a play on words, reminding readers of the earlier meeting between the Dagda and the Morrigan at the river Unshin

133 Then Nuada Aigetláim [Silverarm] and Macha[96] daughter of Ernmas fell by Balor grandson of Neit. Casmael[97] by Ochtriallach son of Indech. Lugh and Balor Birugderc [of the piercing eye] met in the battle. A destructive eye was on him. The eye was never opened except in battle against enemies. Four [men] would lift the eyelid[98] of the eye with a polished ring through the lid. The host that he would see through that eye would not resist against warriors, even if they were many, many thousands[99]. This was the reason it had this venom, that is the druids of his father had been brewing magic potions. He came and looked from the window and looking in the presence of the vapour of the brew, they went into the eye [and] the poison of the brew settled into it.

Then he met with Lugh. [100] It is then Lugh said, "In the end, though he is a small

---

[96] Macha means both a hooded crow and a milking field

[97] Cas – curly hair; mael – close cut or short hair

[98] the word here, mala, is literally eyebrow but in context that seems nonsensical so I am following Gray here and using eye lid instead.

[99] the text here uses two different words in Irish for many: lir and il. It is difficult to render this in English effectively

[100] the following passage, through Balor requesting

man who is striking, whether this is the day of death for you."

Balor said, "On greatly-steady famous-plains under a cloak he rides around meeting for battle a seed I've sown, not a cruel seed myself."

Lugh said, "It was you that brought Lugh, a dissenting burden, come of your seed may my sword be your death, a generous flood my crafts, feats of the Tuatha. Let it be to wolf-packs of Fomorians under floods under stormy seas for them under flood waves what you bring with you. May you not take nuts or milk. May you not take unripe grain or grain, may you not take honour price or honour. No! No! Woe! Woe! May you not end, monster[101], broken wounded the wide world in our little waves, the mighty sea I induce them to cause misery with me. And me, Lugh, do not attack, a two-handed (?) sage carries out a creation {unclear} birth other beings abiding, my body will not be battle-wounded if you bring hounds under many waves. Flowing seas grind battle-people together the sea destroys cruel flesh. Defeat

---

his eyelid be raised is not translated by Gray or Stokes.

[101] aithech can be read as commoner, peasant, churl, boor, or monster.

is a shame on the shoulders of a god. A great flood of the seas will move you. A sword with a Druid, the mind of Lugh, swift wind, howling dragon, shower of fire, fire with me, brightness of sun, brightness[102] of moon."

134 "Lift my eyelid, oh lad," said Balor, "so I may see the talkative man who is conversing with me."

135 The lid was raised from Balor's eye. Lugh cast a sling stone then and the eye was carried through the head. It was his own host that looked at it. And he fell upon the host of the Fomorians, so that twenty seven died under his side, and the top of his head against the chest of Indech son of De Domnann, and a gush of blood sprung forth from his lips.

136 "Bring to me," said Indech, "Loch Lethglas, that is my poet" That is [lethglas] half-green he is from the ground to the crown of his head. He came to him. "Find for me," said Indech, "who threw this cast at me."

[103]"Which iron battle leader, wolflike-iron, who against a branching plough there

---

[102] two different words, lainner and gili, are used for brightness here. Lainner means 'light, brightness, gleaming' while gili means whiteness, brightness.
[103] this portion and most of what follows, barring a

before each equal on me broke the battle against laymen (that is against common people) single-bladed."

Then there spoke Loch Lethglas, "Declare who is the man, a swift boat, powerful, cutter, battle-warrior giving needed explanation fearful-nearness his sling injury-striking undertake boastful breaking of an eye, explain[104] lay bare the victorious-ardour Balor's envious-warrior-fire-man."

Then there spoke Lugh the words-setter[105], answering him, "A man cast without fear without friendship without an opposite number without concealment craftfully equipped. It is me, Lugh lonnbemnach [fierce-striker], son of Cian, son of Ethlinn, it is my growing-power a warrior's eye pouring out battle with great men I break the estate of the Fomorians where noble

---

handful of partial sentences, are not translated by Gray or Stokes. This is because they are poetic forms and both difficult to make sense of and hard to render in English. I am making my best effort here to convey the meaning as I understand it while also maintaining a sense of the spirit of the original.

[104] I am giving toraic here as 'explain' although it more accurately means discovering or giving information

[105] I am taking briatra-sa sis to be briathra 'words' and 'sis' sets forth relates

warriors who took the people in deceptive possession. There is a raven's accusation expecting payment battle-sacred warriors because of a king, a strong drink-portion for warriors subjugated-men knowing anger strong gods bloody their war-spoils to know valorous our battle."

Then there spoke Loch, "Every hundred Fomorian men exceeds [unclear: without nullifying?] with the vigorous fierceness of heroic bands a battle-troop an angry band exceeds dark black venomous-work without sorrow without terror going ample value beneath the Fomorians in Ireland."

Lugh answered, "It is with you," said Lugh, "there are unskilled warriors enduring death jealous they are of the wrathful battle invoking sureties of great heroes a battlefield before the king of the Fomorians threefold Neit."

Then there spoke Loch, "It is with you, oh Lugh half-red [unclear] an overthrowing valuable-flood against them your opposing return travel (?) a path of death to them the cement-sling-stone divided-inheritance host a stream a new-sword renowned their fighting deaths. Without healing wounds immersed in ashes wrath bloodthirstiness after fortunate horseman subdue slaughterous spearmen against a cold band it is not your victory against a sharp edged battle a wolf-poet composing arrangements against them. Not likely a swift ford your wrathful battle that brightness of bloody-plains gore of decapitated corpses."

137 Next the Morrigan daughter of Ernmas came and urged the Túatha Dé to give battle stubbornly and savagely. So that in that place she chanted her poem: "Arise, kings to battle here![106] Seizing honor, speaking battle-spells, destroying flesh, flaying, snaring, seizing battle, seeking out forts, giving out a death feast, fighting battles, singing poems, proclaiming druids collect tribute around in memory. Bodies wounded in a rushing assault, pursuing, exhausting, breaking, prisoners taken, destruction blooms, hearing screams, fostering armies battle, occupants moving, a boat sails, arsenal cuts off noses. I see the birth of every bloody battle, red-wombed, fierce, obligatory-battlefield, enraged. Against the point of a sword, reddened shame, without-great-battlements, preparing towards them, proclaiming a line of battle Fomorians in the chanted margins, helpfully impels a reddened vigorous champion, shaking hound-killing warriors together,

---

[106] From 'Next the Morrigan' to 'Arise kings to battle' is translated by Gray, but everything after through the end of the Morrigan's incitement is not.

bloody beating, ancient warband towards their doom."

138 The battle broke thereafter and the Fomorians were driven to the ocean. Ogma the champion son of Elatha and Indech son of De Domnann king of the Fomorians fell together and were killed.

139 Loch Lethglas asked Lugh for his protection[107].

"Give my three demands to me*!*" said Lugh.

140 "You shall have them," said Loch. "I will remove guarding [against] the Fomorians from Ireland forever and give your tongue a resolution until the end of life on every legal case."

141 Afterwards Loch was saved. It was then he chanted 'the Judgement[108] of Detaining' to the Gaels[109]: "A hold will be affected [against] the bright-company, the lowest people, pillars (?) of earth, every [unclear] great-flower comes to grain and milk, increasing rivermouths, for nuts and

---

[107] the word used here, anacul, can mean a variety of things including protection, saving, shielding, sparing, and giving quarter to. All of these may apply here

[108] dáil is given here as 'judgement' but may also be read as decree, ordinance, or decision.

[109] the section following is not translated by Gray or Stokes.

57

horses a thicket a crowd of oaks, from hearts from swift agreements hidden sorrow, men are given welcome, by my covenant[110] [with] the sun, contesting in noble difficulty. Tradition arrayed men at a feast requires legal binding of equally-angry hearts. The ocean conceals the Fomorians, bright lightning[111], long lived Ireland a strange conditional-prayer, and long life of men fair-sport overflowing today, forever, It will be peace with the Fomorians in Ireland."

142 Loch said then that he would name Lugh's nine chariots because he had been saved. Lugh said then that he should name them. Loch answered, saying, "Luachta [hard heeled], Anagat [protector], Achad [pasture], Feochair [fierce], Fer [man], Golla [foreigner], Fosad [steadfast], Cráeb [branch], Carpat [chariot]."

143 "A question, what names are on the charioteers that were in them?"

"Medol [metal], Medon [middle], Moth [man], Mothach [prolific], Foimtinne [fire-reciever], Tenda [severe], Tres [battle], Morb [dead]."

---

[110] I am interpreting fomcichet here as fom 'by my' and cichet as a form of cich, breast used here poetically to reference an oath of loyalty or covenant
[111] casrao or casar can also be read as hail-stones

144 "What names on the goads in their hands?"

"Not difficult. Fes [knowledge], Res [dream], Roches [great spear], Anagar [protects], Ilach [victory cry], Canna [moth], Riadha [domesticated], Buaid [victory]."

145 "What names on the horses?"

"Can [cub], Doriadha [difficult ride], Romuir [sea], Laisaid [burning], Fer Forsaid [wise man], Sroban [little loaf], Airchedal [poem], Ruagar [very frightening], Ilann much fullness], Allriadha fully domesticated], Rocedal [great song]."

146 "A question, how many are the number of slain?" Lugh said to Loch.

"I do not know how many numbered the peasants and rabble. For the number of lords and nobility and heroes and sons of kings and kings of the Fomorians I know that is three and three times twenty and fifty times 100 men and twenty times 100 and three times 50s and nine times 5 and four times twenty times thousand and eight and eight times twenty and seven and four times twenty and six and four times twenty and five and eight times twenty and 2 and 40[112], with the grandson of Neit among ninety. That is the number of slain kings and nobles of the Fomorians in the battle."

---

[112] Totaling 87,806

147 "As to the number of peasants and low people and rabble and people of every other skill that came in the company of the great-host - because every warrior and every lord and every king of the Fomorians came with dignity to the battle with a host of chieftains, both noble and low-born – I count but a few of the servants of the kings only. This is the number then of those I counted as I watched: seven men seven twenty seven hundred seven five fifty two hundred twenty twenty a hundred hundred ninety including Sab Uancendach son of Carpri Cuilc, son of a servant of Indech mac De Domnann, that is servant to the Fomorian king."

148 "As to those killed who were fighting in pairs and wood warriors [spearmen?] our warriors who did not come to the heart of the battle, until the stars of the sky are counted, and the sand of the sea and flakes of snow and [each drop of] dew on a green meadow and piece of hail and grass beneath the feet of horses and horses of the son of Lir [waves] in a turbulent-sea, they will not be counted at all."

149 Afterwards then they had a chance to kill Bres son of Elatha. He said, "It is better to save me," he said, "than to kill[113] me."

---

[113] guin, literally death from wounding

60

150 "What will happen from there?" said Lugh.

"There will forever be milk-giving on the cows of Ireland," said Bres, "if I am saved."

"I will tell that to our wise ones," said Lugh.

151 Lugh went away then to Maeltne Morbretach [great-judgement], and he said to him, "Will Bres be saved for milk-giving on the cows of Ireland?"

152 "He will not be saved," said Maeltne, "he has no power on their age nor on their bringing forth [calves], even if he controls them giving milk for the length of their lives."

153 Lugh said to Bres, "No, this doesn't save you; you have no power on their age nor on their bringing forth [calves], even if you control their milk."

154 Bres said: "Fierce[114] alarms: Maeltne's action."

155 "Any other request to save you, oh Bres?" said Lugh.

"There is: tell your judge this, reaping a harvest every season if I am saved."

156 Lugh said to Maeltne: "Will Bres be saved for obtaining a harvest every season for the men of Ireland?"

---

[114] ruada, literally dark red but used poetically to mean fierce or strong; may also be read as bloody

157 "This has been an appropriate timing," said Maeltne, "spring for ploughing and sowing, and the beginning of summer through the end strengthening the grain, and the first of autumn through the end for ripening the grain and harvesting. Winter for consuming."

158 "That doesn't save you," said Lugh to Bres.

"Fierce alarms, Maeltne's actions," said he.

159 "Less saves you," said Lugh.

"What?" said Bres.

160 "How shall the men of Ireland plow, how shall they sow, how shall they reap? Knowledge of these three will afterwards save you."

"Say to them, Tuesday their ploughing, Tuesday sowing their seeds in the fields, Tuesday their harvesting."

161 Bres was saved through this strategy[115]

162 After the battle then the champion Ogma found Orna, sword of Tethra king of the Fomorians. Ogma unsheathed the sword and he cleaned it. Then the sword recounted everything it had done, because it was the

---

[115] it should be noted that celg, which I'm giving here as strategy also means deceit, guile, treachery so there is an inherent implication here that Bres was tricking them.

way then when unsheathed [for swords] to reveal the actions they had done. Because of that legacy swords are given the tribute of cleaning them. Further, spells have been kept in swords since. And the reason demons used to speak through weapons then is that they were worshipped by people and weapons were among the sureties[116] of the time.

About the sword Loch Lethglas chanted this poem[117]:

"Good fortune around Orna,
Cold battle,
Corner stone,
Encountering waves
Attaining perfection[118]
And an excellent-wave[119]
Three great lakes
Lake-gap for-days

---

[116] the word here, commairge, is used to mean protection, refuge, security or of people who provide such or who acts as sureties. Its interesting to note that it is here being applied to weapons as if they were considered people.

[117] the following poem is not translated by Gray or Stokes. I am offering my best attempt at the material here

[118] rior can mean top, climax, or perfection among other things

[119] nin can be read as a poetic term for a wave or as a cloud, among several other things

Bright darling
A full quarter[120]
Thirty days
Attacking houses
My frenzied house
The sea[121] silently-stealing
Giving great shaping[122]
The Fomorians of Ireland
Dead beneath Balor
Another fleet of Fomorians dead
The persistent spear of Ethne's son[123]
Every singular attack
Toughened men
Glorious battles
Noble men joined together
Four tracked
A bitter slaughterous tree.
Another known name
Sea of blood
Lamenting cries
Smiting seafoam

---

[120] a three month period of time
[121] Tethrae does mean the sea, among a few other things, but is also the name of the Fomorian king who Ogma got the sword from. Either may apply here.
[122] fodriru is an unknown but I am treating it as a form of fodrechda, although this should be treated as highly uncertain
[123] Ethne's son, that is Lugh who is also known by the epithet Lugh mac Ethne, son of Ethne

Cutting-lamentation
Blood of a multitude of kings
Ogma."

163 Then Lugh and the Dagda and Ogma went after the Fomorians, because the harper of the Dagda had been taken by them, Uáithne[124] was his name. Afterwards they reached the feasting hall where Bres son of Elatha and Elatha son of Delbaeth were. There was the harp on the wall. It was the harp in which the Dagda had bound the music without sounding unless through summoning by the Dagda saying thusly:
"Come Oak of Two Meadows
Some Four-cornered Device,
Come summer, come winter,
Mouths of harps and bags and floods."

Two names were on that harp, that is Dur-da-bla [Oak of Two Meadows] and Coir Cethairchuir [four-cornered Device]

164 Then the harp came from the wall and killed nine men and went to the Dagda, and he played there the three [musics] for which a harper is known, that is the sleep-music and the laughing-music and the sorrowful-music. He played the sorrowful-

---

[124] As a word uáithne has multiple meanings including: a pillar, childbirth, a suture, union, and concord in music. I would suggest in context that last one is the most likely.

music for them so that their sad women wept. He played the laughing-music for them so that their women and their boys laughed. He played the sleep-music so that the hosts fell asleep. And with that charm the three escaped whole - although they wished to kill them.

165 The Dagda brought with him the cattle through the lowing of the heifer from his work[125]. Because when she cried out for her yearling calf the grazing cattle of all of Ireland carried away by the Fomorians as tribute [went].

166 Once the battle was broken afterwards and the slaughter cleaned away, the Morrigan daughter of Ernmas there announced the deadly tidings of the battle and the great victory[126] that had occurred there to the kings of Ireland and to the sidhe-folk, and to the chief waters and to the river mouths. This is why Badb still declares great deeds.

"What news with you?" everyone asked her then.

"Peace to sky.
Sky to earth.

---

[125] referencing the heifer that he was paid with at the start of the story

[126] 1 tasc can also be read as slaughter. Either applies here.

Earth below sky,
strength in each one,
a cup overfull,
filled with honey,
sufficiency of renown.
Summer in winter[127],
spears supported by warriors,[128]
warriors supported by forts.
Forts fiercely strong;
banished are sad outcries
land of sheep
healthy under antler-points
destructive battle cries held back.
Crops [masts] on trees
a branch resting
resting with produce
sufficiency of sons
a son under patronage
on the neck of a bull
a bull of magical poetry
knots in trees
trees for fire.
Fire when wished for.

---

[127] the rest of the poem is not translated by Gray or Stokes

[128] scíath means shields but also "fighting man, warrior, guardian". The usual translation here is given as shield, but I prefer the imagery that comes with warrior, however it may also be taken as "spears supported by shields, shields supported by forts"

Wished for earth[129]
getting a boast
proclaiming of borders[130].
Borders declaring prosperity
green-growth after spring
autumn increase of horses
a troop for the land
land that goes in strength and abundance.
Be it a strong, beautiful wood, long-
lasting a great boundary
'Have you a story?'
Peace to sky
be it so lasting to the ninth [generation][131]"

167 She was afterwards among them prophesying the years at the end of existence, and further promising each evil and lack in those years, and every plague

---

[129] alternately "wished for by flesh"

[130] this line "boinn a mbru" is often translated as "calves in wombs" or something similar, assuming boinn should be boin or boinin - calf, and taking bru as womb. I believe in this case boinn is actually ad-boinn, a form of apad meaning to declare or proclaim, and bru here means boundary or border. I think this makes the most sense in context with the preceding and following lines.

[131] Bidsirnae here is often rendered 'forever' or similar but I am choosing to interpret it as bid sir nae; bid, as a form of atta = there will be, sid = lasting, long lasting, nae = a form of noi nine, also nae people, hence there will be lasting nine [generations]

and every vengeance: so that there she
chanted her poem:

"Something seen is a world that shall not
be pleasing: summer deprived of flowers,
cows deprived of milk; women deprived of
modesty, men deprived of valor. Conquests
without a king[132], pointed, bearded, mouths
of many-oaths, sorrow, a lord without
judgments[133]. Sea without profit. Multitude
of storms, excessively tonsured, forts, barren
of structures, hollow, a stronghold coming
from mistakes a devastated time, many
homeless, an excess of lords, joy in evil, a
cry against traditions, bearded faces[134].
Equipment decaying, numerous exploits,
finding battles, silent towards a spurred
horse, numerous assemblies, treachery of
lord's sons, covered in sorrow, crooked
judgement of old men. False precedents of
judges, a betrayer every man. A reaver every
son. The son will go lay down instead of his
father. The father will go lay down instead

---

[132] Most of the rest of this section is not usually
translated
[133] "feda cin mes" can be translated as "a lord
without judgments" or alternately "trees without
acorns"; given the rest of the sentence is discussing
the difficulties caused by lack of a king, the lord
version seems more logical, but as with most Irish
poetry both are likely
[134] sometimes a reference to Vikings

of his son[135]. In-law each to his own kinsman. A person will not seek women out of his house. A long enduring evil period of time will be generated, a son betrays his father, a daughter betrays [her mother[136]]"

---

[135] The implication being that the son will sleep with his mother and the father with his daughter in law; along with the following sentences it implies a time of rampant incest.

[136] the manuscript ends with "a daughter betrays" with the next page missing, however it is logical to assume the line should be "a daughter betrays her mother"

Made in United States
North Haven, CT
09 August 2022

Situation...Every Time.

Visit mhprofessional.com/perfectphrases
for a complete product listing.

Learn more. Do more.